TOM and JERRY™
Colouring & Activity Book

KU-384-086

ALLI32304
Published in 2014 by Alligator Books, Gadd House,
Arcadia Avenue, London N3 2JU
Printed in Slovakia

The National Literacy Trust is a registered charity no: 1116260 and a company limited by guarantee no. 5836486 registered
in England and Wales and a registered charity in Scotland no. SC042944. Registered address: 68 South Lambeth Road, London
SW8 1RL. National Literacy Trust logo and reading tips © National Literacy Trust 2013. www.literacytrust.org.uk/donate

Dot to Dot

What is Jerry riding? Join the dots from 1 to 36 to find out.

Copy Cat

Use your drawing skills to copy Tom into the grid below.

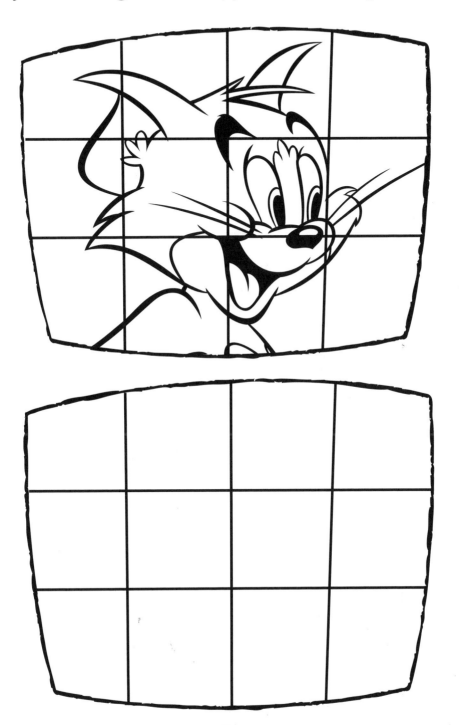

'Mousecapades'

Fit the Puzzle!

Look carefully at the picture and choose the
square that will complete it.

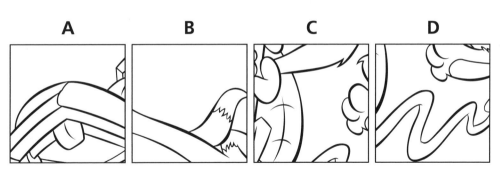

A   B   C   D

Jerry's Super Soapy Slide

Let the Mousecapades Begin!

Run Jerry!

Help Tom through the maze to reach Jerry.

Waking up the Neighbours!

Jerry Scrubs Up

Tom's Bath Time!

Copy the Picture!

Using the image of Jerry, see if you can copy it into the box below. Don't forget to colour it in.

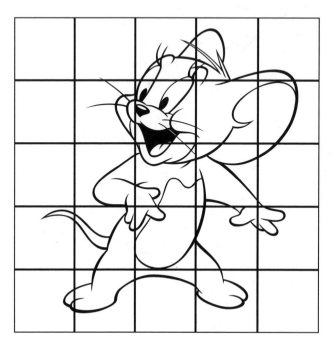

Cool Down

Good Morning, Tom!

A Shower in the Sink

Time for a Bath!

Spot the Difference

Can you find 5 differences between the two pictures?
Draw a circle around the differences.

Yowee!

A Spike Mask!

Dot to Dot

What is Jerry surfing on?
Join the dots from 1 to 17 to find out.

Tom's Ready for a Snack

Nice Mice Dreams

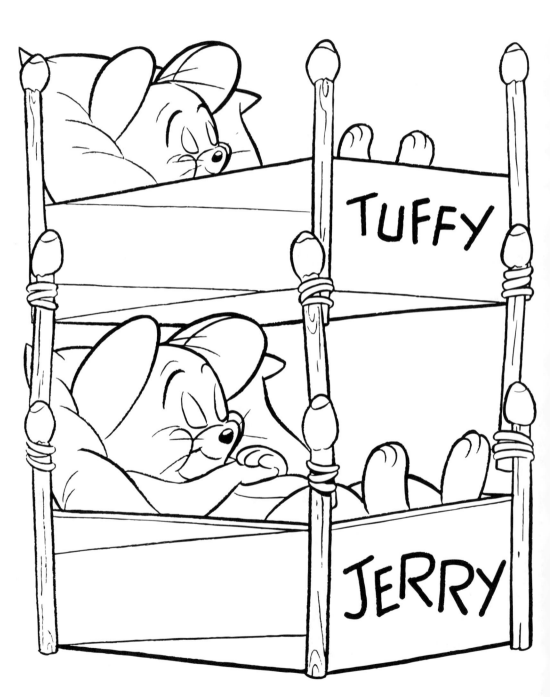

Colour by Numbers

Look at the colour key chart and colour in
the areas with the right colour.

1 = BLUE
2 = LIGHT BLUE
3 = YELLOW
4 = RED
5 = PINK
6 = ORANGE
7 = LIGHT ORANGE

Whoeeee!

A Meat Feast for Tom!

Catch Jerry!

Help Tom through the maze to catch Jerry.

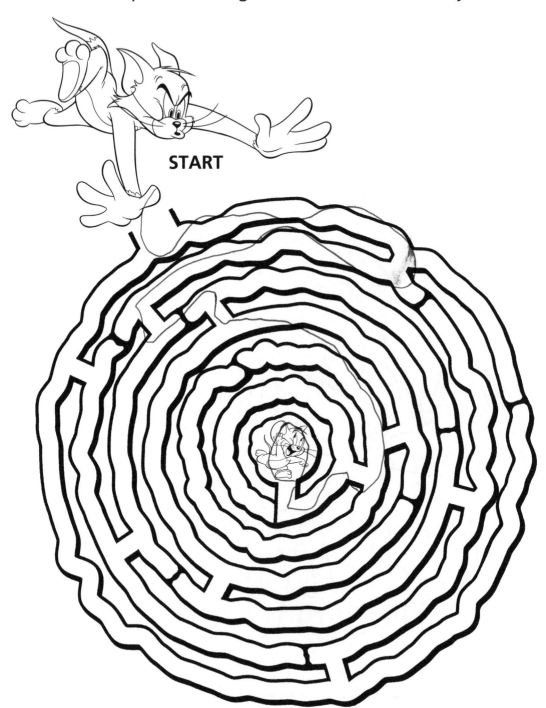

START

Riding the Wave in Style!

Tom has a Great Idea!

Let's Go to the Beach!

Time for a Snooze

Feeling Peckish?

Tom is hungry! Draw Tom some food in the space below. What's your favourite food?

Uh-oh!

What is Tom frightened of? Join the dots to find out.

Fish phobia!

Spot the Difference

Can you find the 6 differences between these two pictures?

The Tom and Jerry Show!

Check-up for Tom

Doctor Droopy

Tom's New Surfboard

Tom's Catnap is Interrupted!

Can you match the two identical pictures of the noisy culprit?

A

B

C

D

E

F

G

H

Now that's what I call a Sandcastle!

This is the Life!

Cat and Mouse

Help Tom catch Jerry by finding the path through the maze.

Uh-oh, Watch out Tom!

Run, Jerry, Run!

Me and My Shadow

Only one of these shadows match Jerry's pose, but which one is it?

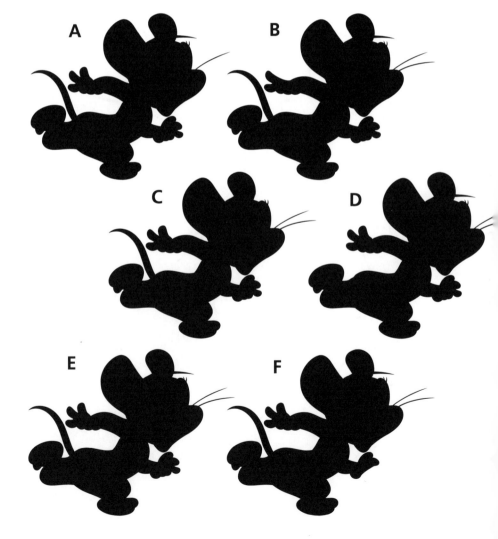

Don't Open that Door!

Can you draw in who's behind the door?

Spot the Difference

Can you find 5 differences between the two pictures?
Draw a circle around the differences.

Let's make Lemonade!

Grab your Beach Things

Dot to Dot

What is Jerry standing on?
Join the dots from 1 to 18 to find out.

Less Mouse-tail, more Cat-tail!

Having a Great Time!

Wordsearch Time!

Can you find these monsters hiding in the grid below?

ZOMBIE
WEREWOLF
DRACULA
GHOST

MUMMY
FRANKENSTEIN
WITCH
BAT

F	O	P	T	Y	C	B	A	T	X	M	Q
R	F	T	G	H	O	S	T	S	Z	K	L
A	T	B	I	X	Q	N	M	O	S	L	K
N	D	M	U	M	M	Y	T	W	V	Q	S
K	V	H	G	P	W	I	T	C	H	J	L
E	Y	T	X	T	E	E	T	S	Z	N	T
N	T	T	T	D	R	A	C	U	L	A	T
S	C	B	T	K	E	H	T	S	Q	I	P
T	T	J	L	T	W	L	R	E	J	K	T
E	T	T	W	Z	O	M	B	I	E	H	T
I	D	F	Q	X	L	I	O	N	L	T	K
N	T	J	H	S	F	I	U	Y	C	N	M

Spot the Difference

Look carefully at the two pictures and circle
the 5 differences between the two.

I love Collecting Shells!

Workout for Tom

A Big Job for Spike!

Relaxing on the Swing

See you next time, folks!

ANSWERS

Pg 2: Dot to Dot

Pg 5: Fit the Puzzle!
D

Pg 8: Run Jerry!

Pg 17: Spot the Difference

1. Jerry's ear is missing.
2. Jerry's eyebrow has disappeared.
3. Jerry's tongue has gone.
4. The seat has turned black.
5. A big bubble has disappeared.

Pg 20: Dot to Dot

Pg 26: Catch Jerry!

Pg 32: Uh-oh!

Pg 34: Spot the Difference

1. Tom's hat badge is missing.
2. Jerry has lost his tail.
3. Tom's tie has changed to white.
4. The information on the fallen letter has disappeared.
5. The shine on Tom's nose has gone.
6. The bottom screen is missing the panel underneath.

Pg 39: Tom's Catnap is Interrupted!
C and D

Pg 43: Cat and Mouse

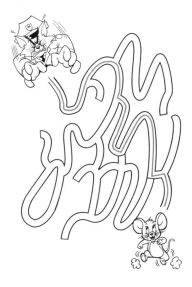

Pg 46: Me and My Shadow
E

Pg 48: Spot the Difference

1. Jerry's ice has disappeared
2. Tom's water has disappeared
3. The ball has one less panel
4. The 'D' in COLD has gone
5. Tom's standing foot is different

Pg 51: Dot to Dot

Pg 55: Wordsearch Time!

Pg 56: Spot the Difference

1. Tom's tongue has disappeared
2. Tom's chest has changed
3. Tom's hair has changed
4. Jerry's eyebrow has disappeared
5. Jerry's tail has gone

Reading Tips

The National Literacy Trust is a charity that transforms lives through literacy. We want to get more families reading. Reading is fun and children who read in their own time do better at school and later in life. By partnering with McDonald's, we hope to encourage more families to read together.

Here are some of our top tips for reading with children.

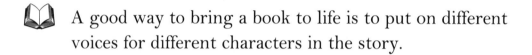

A good way to bring a book to life is to put on different voices for different characters in the story.

Why not stop at certain points in the story to ask your child what *they* think will happen next?

Setting aside some time to read with your child every day is something both of you can look forward to.

A shared love of reading can last a lifetime. You can still read aloud to your child, even when they are confident enough to read by themselves.

If your child is excited by the subject of a story, it will help keep their interest as you read together, so help them choose the books you'll read together.